Surfing on Suicide

BY DANNY STURROCK

Surfing on Suicide by Danny Sturrock

Acknowledgements:

I would first and foremost like to thank Paul and Hilary Kelly for having faith in me and allowing me to tell Simon's story. Your efforts to tackle the issue raised within this play after suffering such a tragic loss yourselves is truly inspirational! Thank you.

I would also like to thank:

'Trig' and Phil Petchey for their time, trust and words. It has been invaluable!

The team at dbda who work so hard and are so supportive of my writing, thanks guys.

Sophie Gorrell-Barnes and all at MBA Literary Agents Ltd

Mark Wheeller and Johnny Carrington for their continued support and enthusiasm.

Kylie for her love and support and for putting up with me sitting in front of a computer screen for hours on end! My family and Karen and Sean for love and support.

Sarah Howell's for allowing us to premiere 'Surfing on Suicide' formerly called 'Suicide.com' at Oaklands.

Everyone at Oasis Youth Theatre (formerly Oaklands Youth Theatre).

Kirsty Spooner, Naomi Wilson, Chris Topliss and Sam Reynolds for being the original 'guinea pigs'.

And last but certainly not least, the original cast:

Charli Well, Anthony Jennings, George Mattack, Sean Gradidge and Mike Mears. Thanks to all of you for believing in this piece as much as I did and for putting your absolute hearts and souls into it, you have played a big part in making this play into something I am really proud of.

ISBN 978 1 902843 29 2

BRITISH LIBRARY CATALOGUING IN PUBLICATION DATA
A catalogue record for this book is available from the British Library.

All enquiries regarding all rights associated with this play, including performing rights, should be addressed to:

Sophie Gorell Barnes, MBA Literary Agents Limited, 62 Grafton Way, London. W1P 5LD.
Tel: 020 7387 2076. Email Sophie@mbalit.co.uk

Further copies of this publication can be purchased from:
dbda, Pin Point, Rosslyn Crescent, Harrow HA1 2SU.
Tel: 0870 333 7771   Fax: 0870 333 7772   E-mail: info@dbda.co.uk

The loss of a child under any circumstances is tragic, but when a young person takes his own life parents, family and friends are inevitably confronted with deeply disturbing issues that compound the grieving process. When Simon killed himself in 2001 our lives changed forever.

One of the issues we found difficult to grasp at the time was the ease with which our son had been able to access information about suicide methods online. Neither did we realise that there were persuasive people in chatrooms who would promote the idea that suicide was the ultimate solution to all problems. Like most people we had no idea that it was so easy to promote suicide in this way.

Danny Sturrock has managed to capture the spirit of Simon. In particular Danny has highlighted his wonderful sense of humour and that of his many friends, so familiar to our family, while also portraying the darker side of the internet that few people experience but which played such a significant part in his death.

In tackling a topic such as suicide there is always the risk of over dramatisation and glorification of the individuals concerned, which could lead other vulnerable youngsters to follow suit. The 'Werther Effect' or copy-cat syndrome is well established in the research literature. We thank Danny for the sensitive and compassionate way he researched this play; he consistently responded to our concerns to avoid unnecessary detail whilst at the same time achieving a play with remarkable dramatic impact.

Although he never met Simon, Danny has shown an amazing insight into our son's apparently normal life. We are also grateful to Simon's friends who agreed to speak to Danny about this terrible happening in their lives.

Sadly, since Simon's death there have been regular cases of internet related suicide, almost all of them young people. The internet is rapidly evolving and has become a vital part in all our lives. It is more readily accessible now than ever before and with new technology comes new safety challenges. After years of campaigning the government and the industry are now more active in promoting safety on the internet. Parental monitoring software is available that did not exist in Simon's day; the law has been updated to make it clear that what is illegal offline - for example the promotion of suicide - is also illegal online; a new body, the UK Council for Child Internet Safety

Foreword

(UKCCIS) has been established. However the difficulty of regulation of internet content based abroad remains and the truth is that internet safety can only be achieved by constant vigilance by us all.

It is our hope that Surfing on Suicide will help raise awareness of online content that has the potential to seriously harm the young and vulnerable. Although the play has a tragedy at its heart we hope the core message is that suicide should never be an option for young people. With the right support those under pressure or with mental health issues, especially adolescents, can and do recover to lead normal lives.

Hilary and Paul Kelly

Surfing on Suicide was premiered by Oaklands Youth Theatre '006' on 16th January 2008 at Oaklands Community School in Southampton.

Full Cast List

Actor	Role(s)
M1	Paul/Tazz/Cypher
M2	Simon
F1	Hilary/Tanya/Jenwolf
F2	Jess/Sophie G

Original Cast

Actor	Role(s)
Anthony Jennings	Paul/Tazz/Cypher
Sean Gradidge	Simon
Charli Well	Hilary/Tanya/Jenwolf
George Mattack	Jess/Sophie G

Rehearsal Images from the original production and Captions

Opening movement sequence with Jess (George Mattack) and Tazz (Anthony Jennings)

Simon (Sean Gradidge) logs onto the chatroom.

Sophie_G (George Mattack), Jenwolf (Charli Wells) and Cypher (Anthony Jennings) and the composite scaffold set.

Simon (Sean Gradidge), Jenwolf (Charli Wells)

The curtain opens with the stage in darkness.

There is one raised area of the stage. The four actors are sitting across the stage on four small square blocks; they are all slumped over in their seats. As the music starts up, (a specially created mix of Daft Punk's 'Technologic' and The Prodigy's 'Spitfire' was used in the original production) each actor 'robotically' comes to life in turn and begins a short repetitive mimed sequence of movement. The music should up tempo as all four actors repeat their movements in sync. Video plays showing quotes about the internet, and highlighting other uses for the internet - online gaming, finding love, etc. These videos should ideally be created in a way that allows the actors to interact with them. Music and video then changes to a more aggressive, sinister mood and the actor playing Simon moves to take up a raised position, centre stage. The other three actors don neutral masks to become other 'faceless' people on the internet.
The faceless then mime various methods of suicide as if Simon is looking them up on the internet, and the sequence should end with a noose being displayed on screen just as Simon produces a real one from under his seat. The faceless ones then exit and the music then fades out. Two of the actors then become Paul and Hilary Kelly.

Paul sits on a chair centre stage while Hilary is moving about tidying up.

Hilary:	*(Calling upstage)* Simon… Simon! These dishes won't wash themselves!
Simon:	*(Under his breath, while quickly trying to hide the noose)* Shit!
Hilary:	Simon!
Simon:	I'm coming.
Hilary:	*(Pause)* He didn't have pudding again tonight?
Paul:	What?
Hilary:	Simon… he didn't want any pudding again. Do you think he's feeling alright?
Paul:	He seems alright to me.
Hilary:	He always used to have pudding…Simon!
Simon:	Alright!

Simon walks downstage and begins miming washing up.

Hilary:	Are you sure he doesn't want to come with us?
Paul:	That's what he said.
Hilary:	I thought he would jump at the chance of a free trip to America.
Paul:	Yeah so did I, but you know what he's like… I doubt you're going to change his mind.

Simon finishes washing up and approaches centre stage.

Hilary:	What have you been up to?
Simon:	Nothing.
Hilary:	You've been in there all morning?
Simon:	I've just been chatting to Tazz online.
Paul:	*(Giggling)* Leave the lad alone.
Hilary:	Are you sure you won't come with us?
Simon:	Positive!
Hilary:	Were not THAT boring are we?
Simon:	*(Giggling)* No it's not that. The truth is, I'm turning the house into a strip club for 5 weeks. Tazz is organising the music and some of the girls from sixth form are going to, shall we say, lay on the 'entertainment'.

Simon rubs himself against Paul provocatively, lap dancer style.

Paul & Hilary:	Simon!
Simon:	I'm joking! … I'm eighteen now, I've never had the place to myself before, plus I get the car!
Hilary:	Well, as long as you're sure.
Simon:	You two deserve a bit of time by yourselves anyway. I'll be fine. Look, I better be off, I'm meeting up with Tazz at the courts. Oh Dad, you can't do me a favour can you?

Paul: What?

Simon: Just finish that washing up will you? It's not going
                     to wash itself.

Simon throws the tea towel over his dad's head and runs off laughing.

Paul: You cheeky little…

The lights fade down in the Kelly House.

The lights fade up to set the scene for the school basketball courts. Two baskets appear at either side of the stage. Appropriate Hip Hop music begins to play as Simon and Tazz enter. They throw down their bags, put on basketball tops in sync and then launch into a stylised basketball match with each other. This should be carefully choreographed to fit the chosen music. The remaining two actors on stage can be used to carry prop basketball hoops around the stage with which Simon and Tazz interact. The sequence should finish with Simon performing a massive slow motion slam dunk in one of the prop basketball hoops. They then sit down, worn out from the match and begin talking.

Simon: You're getting slow in your old age.

Tazz: I'll have you know I'm in my prime.

Simon: A flabby beer belly is a sign of being in your prime now is it?

Tazz: Well, I didn't hear Tanya complaining about it on Saturday night.

Simon: Tanya Morris?

Tazz: What's the matter Si, jealous?

Simon: I don't think so.

Tazz: Oh yeah, that's right. You've got the horn for Jess haven't you?

Simon: No!

Tazz: Everyone knows it Si!

Simon: So what if I have?

Tazz: Then do something about it.

Simon: There's no point.

Tazz: Why not? She's single; you're single, what's the problem?

Simon: What do you mean? There's no problem!

Tazz: That's settled then.

Simon: What is?

Tazz:	Well, you can ask her out tonight. I told Tanya and Jess to meet us down here.
Simon:	I dunno.
Tazz:	Oh come on Si, You're well in there. She's gagging for it!
Simon:	I'm not after sex.
Tazz:	Right! So you're going to turn round and say No if Jess is all like, *(In an effeminate voice)* oh Simon, you're so big and strong. Come on big boy, give it to me, yeah that's it, that's good! Yeeeeehaaaaaaaaa!

By this point Tazz has mounted Simon's back like a horse just as they notice that Jess and Tanya are standing behind them. Simon and Tazz slide across each other into a sitting position and try to pretend that everything is perfectly normal.

Simon & Tazz:	*(Embarrassed)* Hi Jess. Hi Tanya.
Jess & Tanya:	Hi!
Jess:	What are you doing?
Simon & Tazz:	*(Tazz and Simon look at each other)* Well err….
Tazz:	Not a….
Simon:	Working off a bit of… um
Tazz:	Just doing some err…
Simon:	*(Stilted)* Horse… riding?
Tazz:	*(Quietly to Simon in disbelief)* Nice one… dick!
Tanya:	Right!
Jess:	Anyway… Simon, are you doing the technical for the Dance Recital tomorrow night?
Simon:	Yeah, why?
Jess:	Just wondered if you needed a spare pair of hands?
Simon:	Well… ye…

Tazz:	*(Interrupting Simon)* You bet your ass he does! *(Tanya slaps Tazz round the back of the head)* Ouch!
Simon:	Yeah… sure.
Tazz:	*(Singing quietly to himself)* Simon and Jess, sitting in a tree, F-U-C-K-I… *(Tanya grabs Tazz by the ear and starts to drag him away)* Argh! Are you some kind of psycho or something!
Tanya:	Come on you, let's go and find it!
Tazz:	Find what?
Tanya:	Your brain!
Tazz:	Oh!
Tanya:	See ya you two.
Simon & Jess:	*(Laughing)* See ya.
	(Pause)
Jess:	So what do you want to do?
Simon:	I don't mind.
Jess:	*(Jess slides closer to Simon)* We can go for a walk down at the beach if you like? *(She places her hand on top of his)*

Simon's mood changes. He glances down at Jess's hand on his and he becomes agitated and starts to pack his stuff up.

Simon:	You know what; I'd actually better get going. I've um… got some stuff to do at home… see you tomorrow though yeah?
Jess:	*(Confused)* Um yeah… Are you OK?
Simon:	Yeah course, it's just um… See you tomorrow.
Jess:	Yeah… see ya.

Simon exits swiftly leaving Jess on her own, looking awkward.

Jess:	*(Talking to herself)* Nice one Jess. *(She exits)*

Simon enters looking frustrated, throws down his bag. He is alone as his parents have gone to bed already.

Simon: I'm home… shall I lock up?

Silence… Simon sits down, starts flicking through his course work and sits staring at it briefly before tossing it aside in frustration.

Simon: Oh what's the point?

Simon moves to the study where he logs onto the computer. At this point the video images of Simon's computer screen are projected onto the back wall. We see Simon logging onto a website using the alias <SJK> and the opening page displays the message 'Welcome to Suicide-Online …sorry you're here!' As he logs on various people begin to message him and background music plays. These people will appear around him on stage and can be lit by spotlights from above or behind as and when they come online. Their faces should not be seen; perhaps neutral masks can be used.

Simon: Is anyone around?

Cypher: Hi SJK? How you doing today?

Simon: Hi Cypher.

Simon: I've been better actually.

Cypher: What's on your mind?

Sophie_G: Hi SJK!

Simon: Hi Sophie.
                              I'm seriously thinking about CTB.

Sophie_G: What does CTB mean?

Simon: It stands for 'Catch the Bus', which means
                              suicide.

Sophie_G: Oh right.

Cypher: What's so bad?

Jenwolf: SJK, are you about to suicide?

Simon: Hi Jenwolf. I've been thinking about it seriously
                              for the past few months now.

Jenwolf: Same here. I always manage to come up with some excuse not to do it in the end though, which pisses me off.

Simon: I'm just bored.

Cypher: Of what?

Simon: I am bored by everything.

Sophie_G: Have you decided how you're going to do it yet?

Simon: No. I need to do a bit more research first. If I do it, failure is not an option.

Cypher: Here, try this link.

The following hyperlink should be displayed via the multimedia projections. http://suicide-online.com/suicide/methods.doc

Simon: What's that?

Jenwolf: It's a link to a list of suicide methods on the main site that you can use.

Simon: OK, I'll have a look. Thanks Cypher.

Cypher: No worries, I hope it's useful.

Jenwolf: Have you tried any anti-depressants?

Simon: No.

Cypher: Don't bother! anti-depressants are pointless and don't do any good at all.

Jenwolf: Don't listen to Cypher SJK; he obviously doesn't know much about depression. Some people feel lots better with anti-depressant's and some even never have depression again. It's worth a try isn't it?

Simon: Perhaps! I don't know what to do about anything at the moment. Tonight is a prime example.

Sophie_G: Why, what happened?

Simon:	I've fancied this girl for years and was going to ask her out tonight, but it just doesn't seem right to get into a relationship when I'm thinking like this.
Jenwolf:	Just go for it SJK! If you don't it will just be another regret to add to the list if you do decide to CTB!
Sophie_G:	I'm sure I'd feel better if I had someone in my life SJK. I envy your situation.
Simon:	But I don't want to hurt her!
Cypher:	Have you spoken to anyone about how you feel?
Simon:	Apart from you guys on here, no one knows I am anything but a normal happy teenager. People don't realise how good a liar I am.

The lighting cross fades to center stage as Cypher and Jenwolf become Paul and Hilary again and address the audience. Simon remains typing in the background. They should interact with Simon and Sophie_G as much as possible.

Paul:	We didn't know what Simon was doing on the internet.
Hilary:	He was 18. A mature and sensible lad, we took the view that whatever he did online was his business.
Paul:	To be honest, at times I thought that maybe he would be looking at pornography, being a young man…
Hilary:	But to our knowledge…
Paul & Hilary:	He never did.
Paul:	We would have been considerably more pleased if he had been, instead of using suicide websites and chat rooms.
Hilary:	Simon did a lot of research into his suicide. He easily obtained detailed information and guidance on suicide methods from the internet.

Paul: In some ways these information websites are even more dangerous than the chat rooms. I find it hard to believe that this potentially destructive kind of information is so easily available, and that these websites are, at present, deemed to be perfectly legal!

Hilary: We also feel that some of the people that Simon was talking to online were encouraging him to suicide.

Paul: Perhaps not in a direct way… but we see these sites as a kind of club. When you join a club, you tend to adopt there mores, standards and values. They believed that a person should be able to take their own life without intervention from others.

Hilary: If you try to stop someone from killing themselves against their wishes, or even tried telling them not to do it, it could be seen as breaking the rules.

Paul: These are dangerous rules, and ones that played a big part in our son's death. There was no one willing to raise the alarm.

Section 4   The Big Apple goes pear shaped

The action now moves into the school library where Simon is trying to do some of his overdue coursework, but is being sidetracked by chatting to people on the suicide chat room. There is a librarian sitting and typing up some documents. This character is to be played by the actor playing Hilary. Tazz enters and sneaks up behind Simon, who is startled and very quickly closes down the suicide chat room.

Tazz:	*(Shouting behind Simon's back.)* Boo!
Simon:	*(Startled)* Jesus Tazz, don't do that!
Librarian:	*(To Tazz)* Shh!
Tazz:	What's that you've just closed down then, eh?
Simon:	Nothing.
Tazz:	Yeah right. Have you been chatting up the ladies online again?
Simon:	No!
Tazz:	Was it Jess?
Simon:	What? No!
Tazz:	*(Lowering his voice and looking around comically to check that no one is listening)* It wasn't... gay porn again was it?
Simon:	*(Shouting)* Tazz!
Librarian:	Shh!
Tazz:	*(Laughing)* S'OK mate I'm only pulling your leg. So how did it go with Jess at the dance recital last night then?
Simon:	*(Grinning)* It was alright.
Tazz:	Just alright?... You're grinning like a Cheshire cat. Did you do it?
Simon:	No! I told you, I'm not after sex.
Tazz:	Are you mental or something?
Simon:	No.

Tazz:	Well, trust me, if me and Tanya were alone in a small room together all night, she wouldn't be able to keep her hands off me.
Simon:	OK mate.
Tazz:	Yeah... I can see it now....

Tazz appears entranced as he begins to daydream about an encounter with Tanya

Simon:	Tazz?... Earth to Tazz.... *(Clicks his fingers in front of him)*

The lighting changes to set a surreal mood for love as a remix of 'Kiss' by Tom Jones and the Art of Noise fades up. Tanya enters and beckons Tazz over with her finger. A short sequence follows with Tanya and Tazz flirting with one another. As their lips are about to meet Tazz is awakened from his daydream by Simon shouting.

Simon:	Tazz!!!!!!
Tazz:	Sorry mate... so, come on, what happened?
Simon:	Well, when she arrived she looked HOT and I'm talking 'surface of the sun times 10' kinda hot!
Tazz:	Oh yeah!
Simon:	Anyway, we couldn't really talk much during the show but once it had finished...

Simon looks entranced as 'Gold' by Beverley Knight fades up and the lighting changes once again to set the mood for love. Jess enters and Simon walks over to join her. A short sequence follows in which Jess and Simon are clearing lights away, and as they both go to pick up the same one their eyes meet and the following dialogue is spoken.

Simon and Jess:	Sorry!
Simon and Jess:	It's OK!
Simon and Jess:	Jinx!
They both laugh.	
Simon:	Thanks for helping tonight.

Jess:	No worries, I like being with you.
Simon:	You too.

There is a short pause before the pair then moves in for a kiss. Just as their lips are about to meet, Tazz walks over and comes between them, leaving Simon's lips only inches from his. Jess exits and the daydream ends.

Tazz:	So did you kiss her?
Simon:	Of course!
Tazz:	Any good?
Simon:	The best!
Tazz:	Good man!
Simon:	What are you doing here anyway?
Tazz:	Oh, yeah. My mum picked up a load of brochures on holidays to America for us and I thought we should have a look and decide where we want to go.
Simon:	What, now?
Tazz:	Why not? We've both got free periods.
Simon:	Yes, to REVISE!
Tazz:	*(Laughing)* That's a joke right? *(There is a slight pause until he realises that Simon wasn't joking)* Yeah whatever, anyway, I was thinking that we could start…
Simon:	Isn't it just a bit early to start planning it now? It's not going to be for another year yet!
Tazz:	Oh come on mate, we've been talking about this for years. Won't it be cool to know that it's all booked and paid for? It'll be something to look forward to!
Simon:	I know but… I need to revise, it's my last exam tomorrow.

Tazz:	Si, you don't need to revise, you always pass everything.
Simon:	*(Almost under his breath)* Yeah, well not this time… Look… Come round to mine later and we'll have a look then OK?
Tazz:	Oh alright. *(He starts to leave)* Eh, just imagine it… me and you on Venice Beach surrounded by sun kissed clones of Pamela Anderson.
Simon:	See ya Tazz!
Tazz:	Yeah, see ya mate. *(Singing to the tune of James Brown's 'Living in America' as he exits.)* We're going to A-mer-i-ca!
Librarian:	Shh!
Tazz:	You little minx! *(Slapping the librarian's bum)* Sorry!

The librarian at first looks shocked, but then gives Tazz a flirtatious look and chases after him off stage. The scene pauses as Tazz re-enters and turns to look at Simon. Tazz turns to address the audience.

Tazz:	You couldn't say that Simon was a poor student because he was the most intelligent person I knew. And you couldn't say that his social or home life was bad, because it wasn't. To us he seemed to love life and was happy all the time. *(Pause)* We used to have a real laugh. I remember one time at our prom to celebrate the end of sixth form. Simon made a bet with me that he could pull one of our maths teachers.

Tanya enters as Simon's Maths teacher. The lighting changes to set the mood for the prom. Simon is dancing with the teacher in the background with a drink in his hand and chatting her up.

Tazz:	She was one of those teachers that you could have a real laugh with, and she would always chat to us, and she was dancing with us all at the prom. We were all pretty drunk anyway and then about half way through the night I saw Simon talking to her so I started getting pretty

worried, because Simon had said beforehand that he was totally going to go for it! By that time I was feeling pretty sick so I ran off to the toilets to throw up, and when I was in there I heard two blokes walk in, talking about the bet.

Tanya and Jess become Blokes 1 & 2

Bloke 1: Have you heard about this bet this guy's got on about trying to pull his maths teacher?

Bloke 2: Yeah, I know. Apparently he's fully going for it!

Bloke 1: Well I've just heard that he's going to pay her a bribe to do it!

Tazz throws up in the toilet again!

Bloke 2: Seriously? Oh, I've got to see this!

Jess exits and Tanya returns to become the Maths teacher again.

Tazz: Then the two blokes left and I'm now thinking… SHIT! You see Simon had just bought about 250 quid's worth of stuff for his computer and the bet was that if he went through with it, then I would have to pay for it. So obviously a 50 quid bribe to Simon wouldn't have mattered that much! I ran out of the toilets only to find Simon slow dancing with her, trying to wind me up. But luckily… he never did it! But that's the kind of guy he was, he was always up for a laugh… always.

Tanya exits. The lighting changes to set the scene for the Kelly's living room once again. Tazz also exits and re-enters as Paul and begins tidying up. Simon enters.

Paul: Hiya son. Did you get much coursework done at the library?

Simon: What? … Oh coursework, yeah quite a bit thanks Dad.

Paul: Good. Oh, before I forget. A letter came for you earlier. It's on the table.

Simon: Oh right.

Simon goes to pick it up and puts it back down again.

Paul:	Well, aren't you going to look at it? *(Picking the letter up)* It's got a university stamp on it.
Simon:	I don't think I'm going to go to Uni now.
Paul:	What? Why not?
Simon:	I doubt I'm going to get the results I need so there's no point.
Paul:	Don't be daft. You may not get straight A's, but there will be loads of Universities you can get into. Is there something else?
Simon:	What do you mean?
Paul:	Is there another reason why you don't want to go?
Simon:	No… look, I probably will go… I just need to figure out which ones to go for.
Paul:	Well, I'll leave it on the side.
Simon:	Cheers Dad. I'll have a look later.
Paul:	Right, well I'm just off to pick your mother up. See you a bit later.
Simon:	Yeah, see ya Dad.

Paul exits. Simon goes back to pick up his letter and contemplates opening it but doesn't. He rips the letter in half and throws it in a bin. He then walks over to his computer and logs onto the chat room once again. Cypher and Jenwolf enter and sit themselves around Simon. The dialogue from this chat is then spoken and also displayed as text via the video projection, with the accompanying music used previously.

Simon:	Hi Cypher.
Jenwolf:	Hi SJK!
Simon:	Hey Jenwolf.
Jenwolf:	How have you been feeling?

Simon:	I thought that maybe things could get better, but I'm just kidding myself.
Cypher:	What do you mean? What's happened?
Simon:	I've failed my life.
Jenwolf:	But you're so young, at least I think you are.
Cypher:	You're life should just be getting started.
Simon:	I'm male and 18. The typical high risk group.
Jenwolf:	It's sad that you feel that way Simon, but I'm not going to sit here and tell you that things will get better.
Cypher:	But they might.
Simon:	And they might not Cypher! Besides, I've already decided... I'm going to CTB... There are no more options left.
Jenwolf:	When are you going to do it?
Simon:	My parents are going on holiday tomorrow for 5 weeks to America, so it will be in the days before they get back.
Cypher:	Why so long?
Simon:	There are things I need to do first.
Cypher:	Like what?
Simon:	I need time to prepare. I'm going to build a website to act as my suicide note.
Jenwolf:	You've put a lot of thought into this haven't you SJK?
Simon:	Yes, I have. I also want to experience the freedom of a free house and the independence of having the car to myself.
Jenwolf:	Well, we are here to support you in whatever you decide.

Simon:	Thanks Jenwolf. But as I said, my mind is already made up. Anyway, I better be off. I am driving my parents to the airport in the morning.
Cypher:	Are you seeing them off?
Simon:	Yes.
Jenwolf:	What are you going to say to them?
Simon:	Nothing. I don't want them to suspect anything is wrong, but it won't be easy.
Jenwolf:	Well I hope you find the strength you need tomorrow SJK.
Simon:	Thanks Jen. Thanks for talking.
Cypher:	No worries. Remember, if your suicide fails, know that you will be welcomed back with open arms.
Simon:	Thanks Cypher, but it will work… failure is not an option.

The lights fade as sound effects of a busy airport terminal fade up.

Section 5   So much to do... so little time

Paul and Hilary enter carrying hand luggage and suitcases. They are at the airport. Simon, who is also carrying a large suitcase, joins them.

Paul: Right, now all the phone numbers you need are written down next to the phone OK?

Simon: Yes Dad.

Paul: And you're OK for money?

Simon: Dad, I'll be fine. You're worse than Mum.

Hilary: I'm not that bad.

Simon: Mum, I found about thirty Post-It notes slapped all round the house this morning.

Hilary: Well, you'll need to know how things work. *(Pulling out another Post-It note and writing on it.)* Oh, and before I forget, that ham in the fridge needs to be eaten by Friday.

Simon: It'll be alright. If it starts going furry, I'll just shave it!

Hilary hands Simon the Post-It note.

Paul: Don't wind her up.

Simon: Stop worrying, I'm a big boy now. Anyway, you better go or you'll miss check in.

Paul: OK, but don't forget, when we get back you need to go to Gatwick not Heathrow.

Hilary: He knows Paul, now come on. *(Moving towards Simon and hugging him.)* Look after yourself Simon and have fun. We'll call you when we get there.

Simon: Have a great time and look after the old man won't you.

Hilary: I'll try and control him.

Paul: I am here you know!

Simon:	Group hug! *(Simon throws his arms around his father and mother and hugs them tightly momentarily)*
Hilary:	OK, leave some breath in us.

Simon begins to show signs that he is becoming emotional and seems in a hurry to get away.

Simon:	Look after each other OK.
Paul:	You feeling alright?
imon:	Yeah fine. Look I better go, I want to beat the traffic.
Hilary:	OK son. See you in 5 weeks.
Simon:	See you… see you.

Paul and Hilary both wave to Simon as he leaves but he does not look back at them.

Hilary:	See, he can't wait to get rid of us.
Paul:	Come on, let's go check in.

Paul and Hilary grab their cases and exit. Once they have left the stage Simon reappears and looks across to where they have just left and sighs heavily. Simon stands silent for a moment before his mobile phone rings. He composes himself and answers the call.

Simon:	Mum, I promise I'm not really going to shave the ham... Oh Tazz it's you …Yeah, I'm OK mate. Listen. What you got planned for the next couple of days… How do you and the girls fancy a little road trip?

Music suddenly fades up. A mix of the French National Anthem and 'Can Can Can' from 'Moulin Rouge' was used in the original production. Simon, Jess, Tazz and Tanya run onto the raised area of the stage and use four small blocks to create a car. Video images play in the background of various sights in France as if they are driving around. This should be a carefully choreographed stylised sequence which shows the group sightseeing, visiting French shops and buying Baguettes etc, perhaps riding bikes across the stage, wearing onions round their necks etc. It should end with Tanya and Jess huddled around a phone box. Tanya is phoning a French tourist information line to try and find out where there are any cheap bed and breakfasts. None of them can speak French. Tazz and Simon re-enter and walk over to Jess.

Simon: Who's she on the phone to?

Jess: The French tourist board, trying to find a cheap bed and breakfast.

Tazz: Oh, right... I didn't know Tanya could speak French.

Jess: She can't!

They all turn to look at Tanya who is clearly getting wound up with the language barrier.

Tanya: What? Look I.. want... une.. cheapo bed a la breakfast sil vous plait!! Me no speak le Francais!... What?...Look, there's no point shouting at me in French... What?... Bed and breakfast... comprende?

Jess: You do know that comprende is a Spanish word don't you?

Tanya: *(Clearly showing that she didn't know)* Yes!... No! Well, you get some sense out of her then!

Tazz: *(He coughs to get their attention)* Let the Tazzmeister handle this ladies.

Simon: *(In disbelief)* You speak French?

Tazz: Watch and learn... *(Tazz picks up the phone and begins to speak to the operator in English, but with a very bad French accent that gradually merges into an equally bad Italian accent!)* Allo, Bonjour. We, zat eez my friends and I, would like an er otel weech does nota costa mucha. Can you elp us?

Simon: Err, Tazz, what are you doing?

Tazz: What does it look like I'm doing?

Simon:	Well it sounds like your auditioning for Allo Allo!
Tazz:	It's French…duh!
Simon:	No it isn't, it's English with a silly voice.
Tanya:	Um people, we may have to scratch the Bed and Breakfast idea.
Jess:	Why?
Tanya:	We're skint! We spent the last of the cash on all the booze.
Simon:	We must have some money left.
Tanya:	Yep, we've got nine euro's.
Jess:	How much is that?
Simon:	About six quid I think.
Tazz:	Great, and we need food! What can you buy with nine euro's?!

They all look at one another with the same idea in mind and then run off stage. They all re-enter with sticks of French bread as the lighting changes to set the mood for nightfall. The setting has now changed to a field on the outskirts of town. They have parked the car in it and are going to spend the night there. They have all started to drink the supplies they purchased at the hypermarket and are slowly getting more and more drunk.

Tazz:	It's surprising how much bread you can get for nine euro's!
Simon:	Hey Tazz, check this out.

Simon begins waving his baguette around pretending that it is a lightsaber. He begins making appropriate sound effects. They then re-enact the fight scene between Luke and Darth Vader from The Empire Strikes Back with their baguettes.

Tazz:	*(Trying to imitate Darth Vader)* The force is strong in you Luke Breadwaver… but you are not a Jedi yet.
Simon:	I'll never join you!

Tazz:	Obi-Wan never told you what happened to your father.
Simon:	He told me enough! It was you who killed him.
Tazz:	No. I am your father.
Simon:	Noooooooooooooooooo!

Simon falls to his knees as Tazz hits him with the lightsaber baguette. The group begin to settle down to sleep for the night.

Tanya:	I can't believe we've got to spend the night in a field.
Jess:	Oh I dunno! It's quite a laugh!
Tanya:	We're surrounded by cow shit!
Simon:	It's only for a few hours, we'll be home before you know it!
Tanya:	Well, I don't like cows! They're evil.
Tazz:	How can you not like cows?
Tanya:	OK then, they don't like me. I got chased by one when I was little and I've been terrified of them ever since.
Simon:	Now that I would love to have seen!
Tanya:	It wasn't funny!
Tazz:	Night Tanya!
Tanya:	The cow was huge.

Tanya lies down with the rest of them to go to sleep. The lighting then changes slowly to indicate a gradual change of time from night into dawn breaking. Tanya slowly awakes and finds the rest of the group still asleep. Some of them could be asleep in comical positions on stage. She rubs her eyes and then begins to look alarmed, as if she has heard something in the distance. A sound effect now plays over the next piece of dialogue, of heavy footsteps of an animal in the distance coming closer and closer until finally there is a very loud Moo.

Tanya:	What's that?... Guys?... Jess?... Jess wake up!... There's something in the tree's… it sounds like… A COW! Argh!
All:	*(Awaking, startled)* Argh!

They all run off of stage. The lighting changes to set the scene for Simon's living room again. Simon and Tazz enter. They have just returned from France after dropping the girls home.

Tazz:	Aww... home sweet home.
Simon:	And not a parent in sight!
Tazz:	I have such a hangover.
Simon:	Don't go into work then.
Tazz:	Nah, I've got to… I need the money.
Simon:	What time do you start?
Tazz:	*(Looking at his watch)* 25 minutes ago.
Simon:	Just tell them the ferry was back late. Are you still going to stay here while my folks are away?
Tazz:	Yeah. I'll sort out all my gear and then bring it round tomorrow morning.
Simon:	Cool. Bring all of your DVD's too!
Tazz:	OK mate, will do. Suppose I better shoot off but I'll see ya tomorrow, yeah?
Simon:	Yeah, see you mate.

Tazz exits leaving Simon on his own. Simon goes to sit as his computer as the lights change and the chat room music begins to play once more. This time, we don't see Cypher, Jenwolf and Sophie_G. We only see Simon working on his website. He reads the entries out loud that he makes onto the site and these are also displayed on the screen.

Simon: OK, here goes... Hi and welcome to the website of my death. If you are reading this then... *(Pause)* then I have died. I have split this website into various sections, please feel free to browse; in fact I encourage all of you to read this site in its entirety. I plan to kill myself by suspension hanging and will inform the police about www.essjaykay.com, which acts as my suicide note. My apologies go out to whoever finds me, I did not mean to cause anyone undue distress, but unfortunately someone must discover my body. I think that if anyone reading this is considering suicide, they could do worse than join www.suicide-online.com, a pro-choice community. They helped me alleviate the only fear regarding my suicide, that of failure.

The lights fade to black as the music fades down.

Offstage doorbell can be heard, but the stage remains dark. Doorbell rings again and the lights fade up slowly to reveal Simon asleep at his PC. The doorbell rings once again and Simon begins to stir. Tazz can be heard calling from offstage.

Tazz: Si… Simon. Wake up you lazy git and let me in… Si!

Simon: Alright, I'm coming.

Simon gets up, turns his pc off and goes to answer the door.

Tazz: God, waking you is like waking the dead.

Simon: Sorry mate I was out of it.

Tazz: No shit!

Simon: Well if you ever need to get in, just pop round next door, they've got a spare key.

Tazz: Oh, right, cool… So… where's the alcohol?

Simon: What? It's only 11am.

Tazz: Might as well start as we mean to go on, eh? It's not everyday your parents are away for 5 weeks!

Simon: That my friend is a very, very good point.

Tazz: Well, what're you waiting for, get the beers out, crank up the stereo, hook up the PlayStation and let the good times roll!

The Propellerheads 'Spybreak' suddenly blasts out as a stylised choreographed sequence begins. This sequence should ideally be accompanied by multimedia and show the antics of Simon and Tazz's four weeks staying at Simon's house. They should be seen to be having 'matrix' style slow motion play fights, playing the PlayStation, drinking, eating, using the computer, perhaps drawing on each other while they are asleep, and generally having the time of their lives! Tanya and Jess should come and go at various times, both on their own and together. The music and action should be interrupted at two points. One should happen halfway through while Tanya and Jess are trying to cook for the boys. They realise that Simon and Tazz have used every plate in the house. The following dialogue should be used for this section.

Jess:	Sorry to interrupt your game boys, but what exactly are you going to eat this meal we've just cooked for you off of?
Tazz:	Duh! Plates?
Tanya:	There's isn't a clean plate in the house!
Simon:	Chopping boards?
Tazz:	Nah, we used them last week mate, remember?
Simon:	Oh yeah. And we used the frying pans last night, didn't we? *(To Jess)* Just improvise Babe.
Jess:	Or… you could just wash up…Babe.

Simon and Tazz look at each other and then laugh out loud, mocking Jess's comment.

Tazz:	Oh come on, there must be something out there to use.
Tanya:	The only thing you've not eaten off is the baking trays.
Simon:	Well, that'll do.
Tazz:	*(Sarcastically)* Nothing left to eat off, pfft. I don't know.
Tazz & Jess:	Men!

The music resumes and the action snaps back into the breakneck pace previously used. The antics should continue for a short time before Jess and Tanya leave for the last time in the sequence and Tazz goes off stage to get himself a drink. The following dialogue should be seriously overplayed for comic effect.

Tazz:	*(Shouting from off stage)* Noooooooooooooo!
Simon:	Tazz, are you OK?
Tazz:	We've run out of clean glasses.
Simon:	What, all of them?
Tazz:	Yes! Even the chipped and cracked reserves!
Simon:	Damn… I didn't see this coming.

Tazz:	What are we going to do Si?... WHAT ARE WE GOING TO DO!
Simon:	Quiet, I'm thinking... *(mumbling to himself)* So, we're out of clean glasses and no one's here to wash up... hmm... well, it's not ideal, but I think it might just be our only chance?... Tazz, go put on some underwear... we're going to Tesco's!

The music fades up again as the pair dash off stage Batman and Robin Style. The music then fades down as the lighting changes to set the scene for outside. The pair re-enter casually strolling along carrying Tesco carrier bags filled with new glasses.

Tazz:	I have to take my hat off to you Si. That was a genius idea. Why wash up, when you can just buy more glasses!
Simon:	Tazz?
Tazz:	What?
Simon:	The ice cream shop we've just passed... don't you work there!?
Tazz:	Yeah, why?
Simon:	Well, it's just occurred to me that you've been staying with me for nearly four weeks and you haven't been to work once!
Tazz:	Oh shit, I forgot about work. Shit, Shit, Shit, Shit! What am I going to do? I'll say I've been ill.. no, no... I'll say um... err.... I'll say I overslept!
Simon:	For 4 weeks? That's not oversleeping, that's a coma!
Tazz:	I'm on a written warning as it is!
Simon:	I think you better go in mate.
Tazz:	You're having a laugh aren't you! Mama Dragonetti will kill me, or worse still sit on me!
Simon:	What?
Tazz:	Give me your phone.

Simon:	Why? *(handing over his mobile)*
Tazz:	I'm going to phone them… *(Tazz taps in the phone number)* yeah, Hi… it's Tazz… Tazz, you know me… yeah, see that's what I'm phoning about. You see its quite funny really because… *(He holds the phone away from his ear as if Mama Dragonetti is shouting at him)*. I'm not sure what you just said but I'm guessing I'm not needed back into work for a while… *(He holds the phone away from his ear again and hangs up.)*
Simon:	So?
Tazz:	Yep… I think we can safely say that I've scooped my last scoop of Mama Dragonetti's Choco Whip.
Simon:	Sorry mate… do you think they may change their minds?
Tazz:	No way, but I'm not bothered. It was a shit job anyway.
Simon:	What was the biggest ice cream you ever sold?
Tazz:	Um… I made a six scoop double cone.
Simon:	How many flavours do they do?
Tazz:	Fifteen.
Simon:	Here, hold this. I'll be back in a minute… there's something I've got to do.
Tazz:	*(Talking to Simon as he exits, leaving Tazz talking to himself)* Where you going?… OK… well, I'll just wait here then… yeah, that's probably best.

The lighting changes to highlight Tazz sitting waiting for Simon to return. Tazz looks up to address the audience.

Tazz:	I really wasn't actually that bothered about losing my job because me and Simon were having the time of our lives… I had no idea what Simon was planning. No one could have known,

he covered it up too well. In hindsight, he did do some things that were out of character. He spent a lot of money… a lot of money, which was something that Simon never did. He was always pretty sensible with his cash. And there was the ice cream… just after I got off the phone to Mama Dragonetti Simon disappeared. I'd been sat there for about 15 minutes when, just as I was about to leave, I could see Simon in the distance, grinning from ear to ear, carrying the biggest ice cream you have ever seen!

The theme from 2001 - A space odyssey fades up as we see Simon enter in slow motion, miming carrying and eating this huge ice cream. The use of mime and facial expression here should be exaggerated for comic effect!

Simon:	Fifteen scoops my friend, fifteens scoops! That's one of each flavour.
Tazz:	Bloody hell Si!
Simon:	They had to sellotape four cones together!
Tazz:	What are you going to do with that!
Simon:	Eat it!
Tazz:	There is no way you are going to eat all of that!
Simon:	Watch me.

The pair exit. The lights cross fade to the raised stage area.

Jess and Tanya enter. They are sitting in Jess's bedroom. Tanya is sitting on Jess's bed flicking through a magazine and Jess is painting her nails. The same song that Simon played in the theatre the night he and Jess got together plays on repeat on Jess's stereo.

Tanya: Why are you listening to this soppy crap?

Jess: It's not soppy! It's our song.

Tanya: Excuse me?

Jess: Me and Simon, it's our song. Simon played it that night at the dance recital.

Tanya: Well, that's all very sweet but can we take it off repeat please before my ears start bleeding?

Jess: Just once more and then I promise you can put on something else.

Tanya: You're really loved up aren't you?

Jess: It's never been like this with anyone before Tan.

Tanya: Well, he seems pretty keen on you too.

Jess: Most guys I've been out with before only ever showed me any kind of affection when they wanted something, but Simon's not like that, he's really sweet.

Tanya: So… like… have you? *(Trying to find out if Jess has slept with Simon yet.)*

Jess: *(Completely unaware)* Have I what?

Tanya: You know!

Jess: Know what?

Tanya: Oh come on!… You know… Have you done the deed? Gotten jiggy with it? Ridden the midnight train to Georgia?

Jess: Have you been sniffing my nail polish again?

Tanya: Have you shagged him yet?

Jess: Tanya!

Tanya:	Well! We would have been here all night otherwise… so?
Jess:	So what?
Tanya:	So have you?
Jess:	I'm not telling you that.
Tanya:	Oh come on, you've got to tell me! Big Brothers finished now so I need some gossip to fill the void!
Jess:	You NEED to stop watching so much telly!
Tanya:	I can't believe you're not going to tell me.
Jess:	Well, there's nothing to tell… yet!
Tanya:	That definitely sounds like you're planning something. Come on, spill it.
Jess:	Well, Simon sent me a text earlier. He wants me to meet up with him tomorrow at the beach, but he's told me come on my own AND he said that Tazz isn't going to be around either.
Tanya:	Do you reckon tomorrow night's the night then?
Jess:	I dunno, but it's the last night that his parents are away too, so it makes sense.
Tanya:	So that's why you're painting your nails, you little minx. So that they look good when you're scratching them down his back!
Jess:	*(Embarrassed)* Oh shut up!
Tanya:	You're gonna have his babies!
Jess:	Right, that's it; I've got a waxing strip with your name on it!

Jess chases Tanya with a waxing strip. They exit giggling.

Sound effects of a busy airport in America fade up as Paul and Hilary enter with coffee cups and sit down centre stage. They are waiting to board their flight back to the UK.

Paul:	I'll tell you what; I'm looking forward to being able to sleep in my own bed again!
Hilary:	I'll second that! I think the seats on the plane are more comfortable than the beds at the Day's Inn... It's been great, hasn't it?
Paul:	Yeah it has. I can't believe it's all over.
Hilary:	Well you never know, maybe we can do it again in 25 years for our 50th Anniversary?
Paul:	*(Raising his coffee cup)* Well here's to the next 25 years.
Hilary:	*(Also raising her cup)* Cheers.

They both take a sip of their coffee.

Hilary:	Simon would have loved it!
Paul:	Yeah, but I'm sure he's had more than enough fun at home without us there!
Hilary:	That's what I'm worried about! ...Do you think I should phone him?
Paul:	What for?
Hilary:	I just want to check that he has remembered that he has to go to Gatwick and not Heathrow.
Paul:	Hilary, he knows.
Hilary:	Well, seeing as we are being delayed for four hours already, the last thing I want to happen is for us to finally arrive and find out that Simon's gone to the wrong bloody airport!

An airport Public Address announcement now plays.

PA: Attention all passengers flying on British Airways
                             flight number BA775 to London Gatwick. Due to
                             continuing technical difficulties, this flight will be
                             delayed for a further 2 hours. We apologise for
                             any inconvenience this may cause. Thank you.

P&H: Terrific!

The lights cross fade to Simon's house again as Paul and Hilary exit.

Simon is starting to tidy up the house and seems agitated and uptight. Tazz has just woken up and stumbles into the living room, still half asleep. He suddenly stops dead in his tracks and looks at Simon in horror when he sees that he is washing up!

Tazz:	What in the name of all things lazy are you doing Si? It's only 11:30am.
Simon:	Tidying up. My parents are coming back tomorrow afternoon.
Tazz:	But we've got plenty of time to clear this lot.
Simon:	I don't want my parents to have to worry about tidying up when they get home.
Tazz:	Mate, they're probably expecting the place to be a tip anyway, you'll only disappoint them! *(He chuckles to himself).*

There is no reaction from Simon at all. His mood has become quite cold towards Tazz.

Tazz:	Are you OK mate?
Simon:	I've started to dismantle your PC and that, so you can start taking stuff back over to your house if you want.
Tazz:	But then we won't be able to use them tonight.
Simon:	You can't stay here tonight.
Tazz:	Eh? How come?
Simon:	Because I need to get this house sorted before they get back.
Tazz:	Well, I'm not going to let you do it on your own.
Simon:	I don't need any help.
Tazz:	Besides, I had plans for tonight. I thought, seeing as it's our last night of freedom before the oldies get back, I'd arrange for a few people to come round.
Simon:	Then you'll have to phone them all and tell them they can't.

Tazz:	You're joking right? Oh come on Si, we should end these five weeks with a bang! We can get some of the others to help with tidying after the party. What do you say?
Simon:	*(Getting frustrated)* It's not going to happen alright!
Tazz:	What is the matter with you this morning? Did you get out of the bed the wrong side or something?
Simon:	No Tazz. I've got loads to do OK. I haven't got time to stand here answering stupid fucking questions. So, if you can just start clearing you're stuff I'd appreciate it, OK?
Tazz:	*(Now Tazz is annoyed at Simon's attitude)* Look, I don't know what has pissed you off this morning but don't go taking your shit out on me OK. We've had a real laugh these past 5 weeks so don't go and ruin it all by being a dick!
Simon:	*(Throwing down his tea towel)* I'm going out. Lock up when you leave.

Simon walks out quickly leaving Tazz wondering what the hell has just happened. Tazz then exits and we see Simon appear again having just left the house. He is clearly upset at having to behave like that to Tazz, but he knows that it was the only sure way to get him out of the way. He is going to let nothing interfere with his plans tonight. The lights then cross fade. FX of the sea fades up as we see Jess enter. She has come to the beach to meet up with Simon. Simon appears and stands looking at Jess for a moment, taking in just how gorgeous he still thinks she is. She doesn't see him at first, but then she starts to text him on her mobile. Simon's mobile goes off and Jess turns around to see Simon standing there.

Jess:	Blimey, that was good timing... I was worried you might have stood me up!
Simon:	No, sorry. I got held up.

Jess:	So what's this all bout, coz I don't see a picnic basket anywhere so I'm guessing were not here for a romantic dinner on the beach? Not unless you got one stashed…
Simon:	*(Interrupting)* I've got to do something.
Jess:	Oh yeah, sounds kinky!
Simon:	Please? Just listen… I need to do this, and you're not going to understand it but … but please try and accept it.
Jess:	Simon, you're scaring me. What's going on?
Simon:	*(Pause)* I can't be with you anymore.
Jess:	What do you mean?
Simon:	I'm finishing it.
Jess:	Please tell me you're joking!?… *(Pause)* You're serious aren't you?
Simon:	I'm really sorry.
Jess:	Sorry!… That's all I get is it?
Simon:	I told you that you won't understand, but trust me you will soon.
Jess:	How the hell can I trust you? Two days ago we were fine and now you're dumping me, just like that!
Simon:	Please don't make this any harder.
Jess:	Is there someone else?
Simon:	No of course not… Look, I think you're amazing, I always have done, but this is just something I have to do!
Jess:	You know, I really thought you were different. But you're just the same as all the rest. What is it then? Are you getting bored of waiting to get me into bed, is that it?

Music begins to quietly fade up. An edited version of Radiohead's 'Creep' was used in the original production.

Simon: No! Look, I know this isn't easy to understand, but it's the way it has to be. It's for the best. I'm sorry… I'm really sorry!

Jess turns and runs off stage trying not to cry. After a moment Simon turns to walk to the raised area. A series of photographs are shown on the video screen of Simon and Jess together in good times, also pictures of Simon and Tazz, and all of them together. During this sequence the action of the scene switches from Simon who returns home to start preparing for his suicide, Tazz who is at home, but still very wound up by Simon, and Jess running round to Tanya's house for comfort. The music then fades out and we return to Simon chatting on the suicide chat room.

Cypher, Jenwolf and Sophie_G sit around Simon. Simon's final chat online begins.

Simon:	Someone talk to me.
Jenwolf:	About what?
Simon:	Anything I guess! Hi Sophie!
Sophie_G:	Hi SJK. How are you feeling?
Simon:	Pretty good actually. In an hour and a half all the pain will go away.
Sophie_G:	Well I'm glad to hear that.
Simon:	Thanks Sophie. Jenwolf, I'm just sending you a private message.
Jenwolf:	Oh… OK?

The lights fade down to show only Simon and Jenwolf. The other actors on stage are frozen. The private conversation between Simon and Jenwolf begins.

Simon:	Hi Jen. Well, tonight is the night. This is my website address. www.essjaykay.com.
Jenwolf:	Are you going to give me time to read it before you off yourself?
Simon:	Yes, I'm not due for another hour yet.
Jenwolf:	What if I don't get a chance to read it until tomorrow?
Simon:	Then I'll be dead, but you can still read it.
Jenwolf:	OK, that was a cheap attempt to stall you.
Simon:	*(Laughing)* Very cheap!
Jenwolf:	Can I ask one question… why?

Simon:	I am staggered by my complete lack of motivation for work. I never used to be like this. It's only in recent years that I have done absolutely no work. This has meant that I will never achieve the goals I used to dream about. I am also completely bored by life at the moment. I know that is a sad thing for an 18 year old to say but I don't enjoy life anymore. Food is tasteless and bland, life is similar.
Jenwolf:	This sounds like depression. Have you still not tried any anti-depressants? Some people only take them for a short while and then everything's cool again.
Simon:	No, it is depression. I've read a lot about it.
Jenwolf:	Death is pretty permanent, are you sure you wouldn't consider trying an anti-depressant or two before dying?
Simon:	Yes, quite sure.
Jenwolf:	Why?
Simon:	I don't want to try.
Jenwolf:	I wish you would reconsider and just try getting some medical help first. Then, if it doesn't work you can always suicide. It's always an option.
Simon:	There are no more options left.
Jenwolf:	Not true!
Simon:	It is for me, as I perceive them.
Jenwolf:	OK… I respect your decision. If you have any doubts, reconsider!
Simon:	I have no doubts.

The lights fade up again on Cypher and Sophie_G as Simon and Jenwolf rejoin the main chat room.

Sophie_G:	You still feeling good SJK?
Simon:	Yup, I feel fine and dandy.

Sophie_G:	Why don't you go and do something exciting for your last hour?
Simon:	I can't. It's the middle of the night here.
Jenwolf:	The best time for excitement I hear!
Simon:	Maybe, but not where I live.
Sophie_G:	Go to the beach. Hear the wave's crash against the shore.
Jenwolf:	He's only got 35 minutes left.
Simon:	I did that on Sunday.
Jenwolf:	Go out and see the stars.
Simon:	It's cloudy.
Sophie_G:	Go for a walk.
Jenwolf:	Listen to your favourite song.
Simon:	I am listening to my favourite songs. I made a special playlist for my death.

A single spotlight fades up to highlight Cypher as he joins the chat.

Cypher:	SJK, are you about to suicide?
Simon:	Yeah. At 2am GMT.
Cypher:	How you doing? You OK?
Simon:	I'm doing fine thanks Cypher.
Cypher:	Well hang in there SJK! No pun intended! Lol.
Simon:	OK, I die in 25 minutes. Here is my website address. www.essjaykay.com My website is my suicide note and at the moment only the people in this chat room know that.
Jenwolf:	I wish you wouldn't mention suicide-online on your website.
Sophie_G:	Me too. Parents tend to go a bit nuts.
Simon:	Really?

Jenwolf:	Parents may try to get us banned.
Simon:	Well, Cypher is in charge, I'll leave it up to him.
Jenwolf:	When this site gets attention, it tends to be bad attention.
Cypher:	I don't really care what's on the site as long as there are no direct links to this site.
Sophie_G:	Normal people won't understand.
Jenwolf:	Only suiciders understand.
Cypher:	Well, from my point of view, there are no links to the site so I don't care. I'm not going to be the one dealing with the screaming parents.
Simon:	OK, we'll put it to the vote.
Sophie_G:	He's only got 10 minutes left!
Cypher:	It's Simon's decision.
Jenwolf:	We will have to deal with all the mess when it erupts!
Cypher:	No voting. It's your call SJK.
Sophie_G:	I guess we have to trust you Simon.
Simon:	OK, it stays as it is.
Jenwolf:	OK Simon, but I think it's a bad idea.
Cypher:	5 minutes left.
Sophie_G:	Are you leaving now?
Simon:	I will be shortly.
Jenwolf:	SJK, take care. Be sure you know what you are doing, and good luck.
Simon:	I have full knowledge of what I'm doing and its final! Before I go I need one person to do something for me. I need someone to call my best friend Tazz in the morning and give him my website address.

Jenwolf:	I'll call whoever you like Simon.
Simon:	Thanks. His number is 07706 593993. He will probably call the police and they will find my body. I don't want anyone else to have to find me.
Jenwolf:	OK, I'll call him.
Sophie_G:	Please know that it's OK to change your mind.
Cypher:	Yeah, we would love to see you back if you do.
Jenwolf:	You're always welcome if it doesn't work out, remember that.
Simon:	I know, but it will. In about 3 minutes time.
Cypher:	Well, good luck SJK.
Jenwolf:	Goodbye SJK. Rest in peace.
Sophie_G:	Bye Simon.
Cypher:	Happy Bus Ride!
Simon:	Goodbye.

Simon gets up from his computer as music begins playing. A remix of Dido's 'Here With Me' was used in the original production. Simon sets an away message on the site which says: "<SJK> is away - dying". As Simon prepares for his suicide various other characters can appear on stage and act out events that have been seen in previous scenes in the play. These images are to symbolise the things Simon will miss.

Things that Simon needs to do as part of his plan are write down www.essjaykay.com on three pieces of paper. He places one on his computer screen, one in his pocket and another in the disk drive of his computer. He also needs to change into a white t-shirt, but before donning the white t-shirt he should write www.essjaykay.com on the front of it. He should also write one note and place it in an envelope marked 'Mum and Dad'. This should be propped up against his computer monitor. Once Simon has finished his preparations he should produce a length of thick rope, which he then begins to make a noose with. Once complete, he should pull on it to test it and then gather up the loose rope and look upwards off stage as if looking to the loft space. He then takes a slow walk off stage, but just before he exits completely, he pauses and takes a final look around his house and out towards the audience. He then exits and the stage remains empty for a short time before the music suddenly stops and the lights snap to black. The words "Simon killed himself shortly after 2am" appear on screen.

Spotlights begin to fade up on Cypher, Jenwolf and Sophie_G. They are all still in the chat room wondering if Simon has actually killed himself. A spotlight also shines dimly above Simon's computer to highlight that he is no longer there.

Sophie_G:	SJK? Are you there?
Cypher:	He's still logged into the chat room.
Sophie_G:	SJK, please respond.
Cypher:	Should we kick him off the chat?
Jenwolf:	Can you imagine what would happen to this site if his computer is found logged onto here?
Cypher:	SJK?
Jenwolf:	Leave it… for now at least. He may need to be here.
Cypher:	If he doesn't respond sometime in the future, we can ban his account.
Sophie_G:	I think he said before that his parents are away on holiday so it gives us some time.
Jenwolf:	but his best friend will know tomorrow morning.
Cypher:	His account says SJK is away, dying.
Sophie_G:	Do you think he's really done it?
Cypher:	He might have done. I dunno.
Jenwolf:	I really had the impression he was going to go through with this.
Sophie_G:	I'm calling someone.
Jenwolf:	Sophie, don't call the police on him!
Sophie_G:	Why not?

Cypher:	Have you really thought about what good that would do if he was caught Sophie? Don't call them.
Sophie_G:	I can't think that he's there hanging.
Jenwolf:	He might be, or he might not be.
Sophie_G:	Shut up Jen.
Cypher:	If he is hanging, then calling the police on him wouldn't do any good.
Jenwolf:	Yeah. Not very cool when he gets thrown into some institution for 9 months and comes out feeling worse.
Sophie_G:	I don't want to call from home. I don't want them nagging the fuck out of me later with questions.
Cypher:	Don't call it!
Sophie_G:	Look, I know I'd hate it if someone called and it was me catching the bus, but shit! I've been sitting here guessing and it is sick!
Jenwolf:	We'll know for sure tomorrow, just relax.
Sophie_G:	I can't wait till tomorrow!
Cypher:	Sometimes all you can do for the best of friends is watch them die.
Sophie_G:	I'd feel guilty.
Jenwolf:	Why would you feel guilty, it's not your choice, it's his!
Sophie_G:	I'm looking his name up in the phone book.
Jenwolf:	Sophie, go to bed! Cypher, my fingers are itching to kick Sophie off the chat!
Cypher:	Restrain yourself Jenwolf.
Jenwolf:	Well I can't have a fucking interventionist in here right now goddammit.

Cypher:	Kicking her off won't stop her from calling, it won't help!
Jenwolf:	Are you going to call it Sophie?
Sophie_G:	Yes!
Cypher:	What good will it do you or him?
Sophie_G:	Fuck you Cypher, I don't care. How can you people be so heartless?
Jenwolf:	Just answer the question Sophie. What good will it do you or him?
Sophie_G:	Because I can't fucking bear the thought that he could be hanging right now while everyone is fucking chilling!
Jenwolf:	I'm not chilling and anyway, people are dying every minute.
Cypher:	Sophie, there isn't anything we can do about it. Maybe you should log off for a bit, take a break and then come back tomorrow? He might not have done it.
Sophie_G:	Fuck that!
Cypher:	Right that's it; I'm kicking Simon's account off the site. If he really is dead, we don't need his computer sitting on here. And if he's alive, let him ask someone to let him back in.

The lights suddenly black out as Simon's account is thrown off the site. Cypher, Jenwolf and Sophie_G exit the stage in darkness.

The chat room displayed on the screen on stage throws up a message saying, 'You have been kicked from the site by Cypher.' This message just flashes on screen before fading to black. A video backdrop depicting Tazz's home then fades up. Tazz enters.

Tazz: *(Calling to offstage)* Alright Mum, I'm coming. I'm just trying to find my keys. *(He scurries around looking for them before finding them on the floor)* It's OK I've got them!

Just as Tazz exits the stage his mobile phone rings on the side. It continues to ring about 5 times before he runs back in and picks it up.

Tazz: Yeah, hang on Mum! *(Answering the phone)* Hello?... *(Pause)* Who is this?

The lights fade to black again and Tazz exits. FX of an aeroplane landing can be heard which then fade into FX of a busy airport. The lights fade up again as Paul and Hilary are standing waiting for Simon to meet them at the arrivals gate.

Hilary: I knew he'd be late.

Paul: Don't worry, he'll be here. He's probably stuck in traffic.

Hilary: Have you tried ringing his mobile again?

Paul: Yes, I've tried it three times but he won't be able to answer it if he's driving, will he?

Hilary: No, I suppose not.

Then an announcement plays over the airport PA system.

PA: *(Recorded)* This is a passenger announcement. Can Mr and Mrs Kelly, who arrived on British Airways flight number BA775 make yourselves known to a member of the ground crew. That's Mr and Mrs Kelly from British Airways flight number BA775, please make yourselves known to a member of the ground crew.

The lighting then changes again as two spotlights highlight Paul and Hilary. They address the audience.

Paul: We looked at each other, but not in alarm at this stage. We made ourselves known to one of the staff and were immediately put onto one of those buggies with a bleeping noise and flashing light. At this point I began to think something must be seriously wrong.

Hilary: I asked the woman what was happening and tried to get more information, but she clearly could not or did not want to tell us anymore. We were taken to a private room. As the door opened I first caught sight of Tazz's Mum, and then Tazz *(A spotlight shines to highlight a distraught looking Tazz)*... they looked terrible. And Tazz said straight away...

Tazz: Simon's dead.

Hilary: I asked, was it a road crash? And he replied...

Tazz: No... he killed himself.

The spotlight on Tazz fades to black.

Hilary: I remember shouting "No". They must have made a mistake... I couldn't believe it... That was until we eventually saw Simon's body in the mortuary.

Paul: When we found out about the websites Simon had been using, again, it was difficult to take in at first. Initially I did not believe that the Simon I knew... intelligent, perceptive, cool with all things technical, could have had anything to do with such bizarre sites.

Hilary: I think that several people thought that because it was on the internet that it was a joke at first. People just found it so unbelievable, because it was just so out of character.

Paul: The people in these chat rooms are all suicidal themselves, so someone one who is suicidal getting advice from someone else that is suicidal surely cannot be a good thing? It can only serve to reinforce those feelings.

Hilary:	We can't help feeling that if Simon hadn't had access to other suicidal people, then he would have stood a better chance of pulling out of his own suicidal feelings.
Paul:	We were also totally shocked to discover that Simon had launched a website for his death only minutes before he died. He had left various messages... *(As each character speaks, they should be subtly lit in turn.)*
Hilary:	To my Parents…I apologise for all of this, as I know it will be you who it affects the most… Please forgive me for what I've done, as I can never forgive myself. I am glad that we were on good terms the last time we met and I shall always treasure your memory… For Jess…
Jess:	I hope you realise now why we had to break up before. I wanted to break up before I died. However much you hurt then… I knew it would be worse if your boyfriend had died. You are one of the few people I have ever truly loved. Apart from that, you have been a great friend. I think you will be successful in whatever you do and I wish you every happiness. For Tazz...
Tazz:	You have been a great mate over the years, especially for the last couple of weeks. I sincerely do hope you get with Tanya, she's a lovely girl. I'm afraid we're gonna have to postpone that trip to America, maybe next life, eh? … Jess…

The music then fades down as Hilary, Paul and Jess sit facing the audience.

Paul:	Lots of young people feel suicidal at some point in their lives. Thousands go into hospital each year having tried to harm themselves. Many more than this try to take their own lives… and nobody ever gets to know about it.
Hilary:	Most of these people recover and never try again. A small number, however, do succeed in

killing themselves. This is why feeling suicidal can be dangerous and needs to be talked about.

Jess: I often think about how well Simon covered up what he was feeling, but I can't help thinking that maybe if he'd just spoken to someone in his family, one of his teachers, his GP or anyone other than these faceless people on the internet, then... then maybe he would still be here today.

Paul: Since Simon's death in 2001 at least 17 people in the UK, some very young, have taken their own lives assisted by suicide websites and chat rooms. There are no official statistics, so this might just be the tip of the iceberg.

Hilary: We have been campaigning with a charity called PAPYRUS - Prevention of Young Suicide, to alert parents and carers to this problem.

Paul: We want the government to clarify the law so that websites that have no other purpose than to encourage the young and vulnerable to take their own lives should be made illegal.

Hilary: Suicidal feelings and depression need not lead to tragedy. With support from family, friends and professional care many people go on to live normal lives.

Music then fades up quietly. Radiohead's 'No Surprises' was used in the original production.

Paul: In preparation for his suicide, Simon had thought of everything...

Hilary and Paul: But... not what he was leaving behind.

The music fades up and the lights fade down on the actors. A series of statistics and positive messages are now projected onto the back of the theatre along with useful website addresses and helpline phone numbers. A list of these website addresses and helpline numbers should be made available for people to take away with them as they leave the auditorium.

Other plays published by **dbda**

KILL JILL by Mark Wheeller

Big Brother meets Kill Bill meets Jack (of Beanstalk fame) meets Tony Martin… Mix these together to create *Kill Jill!* This brand new play by Mark Wheeller explores the topical issues of homeowners defending themselves, and asks "How far can Reality TV be allowed to go?"

Jill is the latest victim of Reality Lottery, a futuristic form of National Service to entertainment. She accompanies Jack as he (again) robs George, who lies in wait armed with a shotgun. The Reality Lottery camera operators are filming everything… but should they intervene? The ending is suitably Tarantinoesque!

ISBN 978 1 902843 20 9

Cast: *11+ (3m, 3f & 5 m or f)*
Suitable for GCSE with doubling (2m, 2f & 1 m or f)
Duration: *50 minutes approx.*
Suitable for: *ages 13+ or adults!*

Commissioned and premiered by The Birmingham Rep Theatre

Kill Jill! raises issues of rights and responsibilities. It is a play full of interesting techniques that will delight Drama teachers and students, and will thrill those exploring Citizenship issues through imaginative and entertaining Theatre productions.

'Kill Jill is a very fizzy ride! What a great script! The playfulness with style and wide range of reference points with an 'anytime, anyplace, anywhere' theatrical freedom… the banter goes to some strange places too - perhaps a Python influence? The build up of tension in the visit to George's castle puts the end of the play in firm thriller territory! Wonderful stuff!!!!!'

Paul Mills, Head of Drama, Westgate School, Winchester

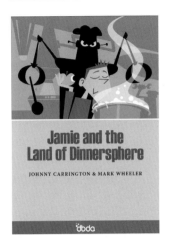

ISBN 978 1 902843 25 4

Cast: *2m and 2f with doubling or 3m, 1f and 5 or 6m/f. Suitable for use as a TIE production in the new vocational courses for ages 13+ (or as a performance piece in Primary schools)*
Duration: *35 minutes (55 minutes with the workshop)*

Jamie and the Land of Dinnersphere (a Healthy school dinners play)
by Johnny Carrington & Mark Wheeller

Jamie Jamjar loves healthy food. He has seen how a poor diet can mess you up… just by looking at his sister… Lazy Lillian! Jamie is shocked when his school tries out the new Robot Dudes (fast food servants) who replace the friendly dinner ladies. Jamie then discovers his own father invented them!

Can it get any worse? Yes it can!

Jamie is transported to Dinnersphere (in another of his father's inventions, a Story Rocket) where Jamie discovers the nefarious Dinnerwitch, busy planning world domination through putrid school dinners! Together with three friends, Bo, Agor and another - a member of the Primary School audience - they confront and defeat the Dinnerwitch!

Jamie provides an opportunity for secondary school students to present an interactive Theatre In Education play with all the joys of the audience being a key part of the final performance. It is expected to become a staple part of the new vocational courses where there are, at the moment, few plays which will fit the specification so well!

The text includes an innovative interactive workshop written by Adrian New (Stopwatch Theatre) which can be led by the secondary students.

Other plays published by **dbda**

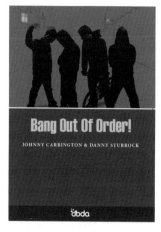

ISBN 978 1 902843 21 6
Cast: 2m & 2f
Suitable for GCSE
Duration: 55 minutes approx.
KS 3 & 4

Bang Out Of Order
by Johnny Carrington & Danny Sturrock

4 friends, 1 secret, 1 chance, 1 life. The play tackles anti-social behaviour head on. This rollercoaster ride will educate, amuse and challenge.

Set on an urban estate, newcomer Ollie has a history of antisocial behaviour and is attempting to reform. His family are forced to move away in an attempt to make a fresh start… but once he is accepted into the local group of youths, things start to go wrong.

The play tackles the sensitive issues using a mixture of comedy, dance, music and multi-media.

'If you are setting out to convey a message, the mixture of naturalism which pulls no punches, stylised movement that moves the action along with wit and mixed media, adds another dimension that certainly grabs the attention of the audience.'

Fran Morley, Director, Nuffield Theatre Southampton

ISBN 978 1 902843 16 2
Cast: 2m & 2f with doubling,
or up to 18
Duration: 45-50 minutes
KS 3 to adult

Missing Dan Nolan by Mark Wheeller

This play, based on the true story of Dan Nolan, a teenage boy who went missing on the night of January 1st 2002, is written in the same documentary style as Too Much Punch for Judy. It has won awards and commendations at every Drama Festival it has entered. It is now, like so many of Mark's other plays, being toured professionally by the Queens Theatre in Hornchurch, Essex.

'Unusual and deeply affecting. Skillfully written… achieves astonishing depth and authenticity… '

Charles Evans, Adjudicator, Eastleigh Drama Festival

Exemplar text for Unit 2 in the Hodder Education Edexcel Drama for GCSE book (2009 specification) endorsed by Edexcel.

Other plays published by **dbda**

ISBN 1 902843 19 3

Cast: 34m, 3f & 2m/f or 2m & 2f
for GCSE
Duration: 35 minutes approx.
KS 3 & 4

Chicken! by Mark Wheeller

A 'new and improved' version of WHY DID THE CHICKEN CROSS THE ROAD? The play tells the story of two cousins, Tammy and Chris. We are led to believe that something bad will happen to Chris who refuses to wear his cycle helmet. It is, however, Tammy who gets killed on the one morning that the cousins walk to school. Chris remains unwilling to tell anyone of his part in the accident and he has to live with this dreadful secret. One of the main changes is the introduction of Chris filming Tammy's fatal dare on his mobile phone camera.

'We have just been fortunate enough to witness the most superb exhibition of interactive safety education. The performance was quite stunning!'

Jim Lambert, Head Teacher Sinclair Middle School, Southampton

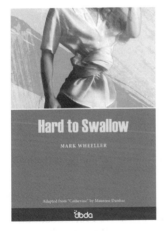

ISBN 978 1 902843 08 7

Cast: 3f & 2m with doubling,
or 6f, 3m & 16
Duration: 70 minutes approx.
KS 3 to adult

Hard to Swallow by Mark Wheeller

This play is an adaptation of Maureen Dunbar's award winning book (and film) **Catherine** which charts her daughter's uneven battle with anorexia and the family's difficulties in coping with the illness.

The play has gone on to be performed all over the world to much acclaim, achieving considerable success in One Act Play Festivals. Its simple narrative style means that it is equally suitable for adult and older youth groups to perform.

'This play reaches moments of almost unbearable intensity... naturalistic scenes flow seamlessly into sequences of highly stylised theatre... such potent theatre!'
Vera Lustig, The Independent

'Uncompromising and sensitive... should be compulsory viewing to anyone connected with the education of teenagers.'

Mick Martin, Times Educational Supplement

Other plays published by **dbda**

The Gate Escape by Mark Wheeller

The story of two truants. Corey is 'addicted' to bunking school. Chalkie views himself as a casual truant "no problem!" While truanting with some friends, the pair are greeted by a surreal 'Big Brother' figure who sets them a task. The loser will be in for some dramatic 'Big Bother'... Who will lose?... What will this 'bother' be?

The play has toured professionally throughout the south of England to great acclaim.

'A lively dramatic style and innovative structure with dynamic and contemporary dialogue. It is written in a way to guarantee that the audience will feel fully involved and enthralled by the main characters.'

Professor Ken Reid, Author of Tackling Truancy in Schools

'Theatrically interesting... excellent basis for active discussion of issues and dramatic style with reluctant GCSE students'

Ali Warren (National Drama)

ISBN 978 1 902843 22 3

Cast: *2f & 2m with doubling, or up to 30*
Duration: *70 minutes*
KS 3 & 4

Heroin Lies by Wayne Denfhy

A sensitive, yet disturbing look at drugs and drug dependency, in particular the pressures and influences at play on an ordinary teenage girl. We observe Vicki's gradual and tragic slide towards addiction and also the various degrees of help and hindrance she receives from family and friends.

This is a new, updated edition of Wayne Denfhy's popular play. It is suitable for performance as well as for reading in the class. Included with the playscript is an excellent scheme for follow-up work by Peter Rowlands.

'...a piece of drama that will stimulate and challenge a young cast... Heroin Lies deals with vital issues that affect today's youngsters in a gentle and humane way and, in so doing, gets its message across without the instant rejection that can meet other approaches.'

Pete Sanpher, Head of Drama, Norfolk

ISBN 1 902843 15 0

Cast: *8f, 7m and 2m/f*
Duration: *70 minutes approx.*
KS 3 & 4

Other plays published by **dbda**

ISBN 1 902843 17 7

Cast: 33f, 3m &3m/f or 3m & 3f
for GCSE using suggested cuts
Duration: 55 minutes approx.
KS 3 & 4.

Gagging for it by Danny Sturrock

Summer is here, A-levels are over and a group of 6 friends embark on a holiday to Ibiza! What would their holiday bring? Would Chris finally pluck up the courage to ask out Teresa? Would Jay drink himself into oblivion? Would Bianca spend the entire holiday flirting with the Spanish barmen – more than likely! …or would their experiments with drugs bring their hedonistic worlds crashing down around them!?

Comedy, dance, music and choreography are the keys to this production. The pace is breakneck and hilarious, but once the party's over, it hits you!

'Really funny… laugh out loud funny. Inspired outstanding performances from the six Year 11s who went on to exceed our expectations by a long way in their GCSEs achieving A or A*. It proved to be a firm favourite with our KS3/4 audience.'

Mark Wheeller

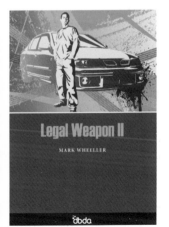

ISBN 978 1 902843 18 6

Cast: 32f & 2m with doubling
Duration: 60 minutes approx.
KS 3 & 4 and A Level

Legal Weapon II by Mark Wheeller

This is a new "improved" version of the popular Legal Weapon play which is touring schools across the UK.

It is the story of a young man, Andy. His relationship with his girlfriend – and his car – are both flawed, but his speeding causes the loss of a life and the loss of his freedom.

In Legal Weapon II, the story takes an additional twist when Andy realises that the person he's killed is somebody very dear to Jazz, his girlfriend.

Legal Weapon II promises to be faster, funnier and far more powerful!

'A gripping storyline. Even the most challenging of our students were held by the drama. This learning experience should be given to each Year 11 as they come through the school.'

Myrtle Springs Secondary School

Other plays published by **dbda**

ISBN 978 1 902843 05 6

Cast: *3f, 3m & 6 or 2m & 2f with doubling*
Duration: *45 minutes approx.*
Suitable for: *ages 14+*

Too Much Punch For Judy
by Mark Wheeller

May 20th 1983... a lonely road near Epping... a car comes off the road and hits a bridge. The scaffolding construction slices through the car. The driver, Judy, escapes unhurt, but the passenger, her sister, Joanna is killed outright. Joanna and Judy were on their way home from an aerobics session followed by a trip to the local Wine Bar. They had both been drinking.

This tragic incident was dramatised by Mark Wheeller in 1986 using only the words of those most closely involved and affected. Since that time it has become one of the most performed plays ever. This version of the script is revised.. and updated with a further tragic incident.

"The play will have an impact on young people or adults. It will provoke discussion. It stimulates and wants you to cry out for immediate social action and resolution."
Henry Shankula – Addiction Research Foundation, Toronto

"The young audience I was sat in was patently out for some whooping Friday night fun... at the end there was a horrid silence."
Nick Baker – Times Educational Supplement.

"A formidable attack on drunken driving."
Pru Kitchen – The Scotsman

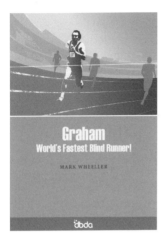

ISBN 978 1 902843 26 1

Cast: 6 (3m, 3f with doubling).
Can be performed with a cast
of up to around 30. (10m, 8f &
12 m or f)
Duration: 55 minutes
Suitable for: ages 13+
or adults!

Developed from Mark
Wheeller's stage play Race
To Be Seen, written with the
Epping Youth Theatre.

Available on DVD, the
award winning Oaklands
Youth Theatre production.
For more information
contact dbda.

Graham – World's Fastest Blind Runner! by Mark Wheeller

Written in the same documentary style as Too Much Punch For Judy, Mark's first version of this play about Graham Salmon MBE, was awarded Critics Choice at the Edinburgh Festival Fringe (1984).

It has recently been re-written, and on it's first two outings won through to the Final of both the National Drama Festivals Association in 2007 and the All England Theatre Festival in 2008, winning different awards at each Festival.

Listed in the Guiness Book of Records as The Worlds Fastest Blind Runner in 1976 (100m in 11.4 secs) Graham went on to play Golf for the international visually impaired team for whom he hit a famous "hole in one" in The British Open!

"I didn't ever need convincing that 'Graham' was an ideal piece to challenge my group and that it ticked all the boxes for A-level work, but if I ever needed justification, then the results have certainly given it. In the breakdown of the Unit 2 marks i.e. the performance of 'Graham', all seven candidates were awarded 100%. It's worth noting that the external moderator was accompanied that evening by her senior examiner! Thanks again for the material and thanks to Graham, such an inspirational person!"

Mike Fleetwood, Parkside Arts College.

Selected as an exemplar Unit 2 study text in the Longman/Pearson 2009 Edexcel GCSE Drama Teacher and Student book.

Script & Lyrics by Mark Wheeller
Music by James Holmes

Wacky Soap

The Music Score

Includes a Mini-Musical for Junior Schools

ISBN 1 902843 06 1

The full version of the Musical play which includes scheme of work for KS3/4.

Wacky Soap by Mark Wheeller

Wacky Soap is a Pythonesque allegorical tale about 'substance' abuse (drugs, alcohol, glue, tobacco, etc). While washing with Wacky Soap leads to instant happiness and an inclination towards outrageous behaviour, prolonged use washes away limbs and ultimately leads to dematerialisation. This has become a tried and tested (and increasingly popular) School/ Drama Club/ Youth Theatre production and is an ideal vehicle for a cast of any age.

'Wacky Soap is a brilliant show for any age group. It has the "Wow factor" not the "Yawn factor" so often associated with educational material. The script is fast and comical. The songs are wonderfully catchy. The Audience at the end were calling for more'.

Sally Dwyer, Hants Drama Teacher/ Eastleigh Borough Youth Theatre Director

---

The story of Wacky Soap first appeared as a full **Musical play.** A mini version of the play is included with the **Music Score.** The **Storybook**, as well as being a wonderful book to read on its own, is often used for inspiration with props and costumes for the play. **A Past-performance CD** gives you the opportunity to hear the songs of the play, while a fully orchestrated **Backing track CD** is invaluable for those who want to produce the play but do not have music facilities.

ISBN 1 902843 07 X

A fully illustrated book with the story of Wacky Soap in narrative form.

ISBN 1 902843 02 9

*A companion book with the Music Score and a **Mini-Musical** version of the play.*

Past Performance and Backing track CDs
